NIGHTMARE
OF THE
SCARECROWS

WRITTEN BY IAN MacDONALD
ILLUSTRATED BY MARK PENMAN

Titles in Graphic Novels set

KANE STRYKER, CYBER AGENT
BY ROGER HURN & AMIT TAYAL

NIGHTMARE OF THE SCARECROWS
BY IAN MacDONALD & MARK PENMAN

THE HEAD IS DEAD!
BY TOMMY DONBAVAND & MARK PENMAN

THE COLONY
BY TOMMY DONBAVAND & KEVIN HOPGOOD

SPACE PIRATE UNICORN
BY DANNY PEARSON & PETER RICHARDSON

TERROR SWIPE
BY JONNY ZUCKER & PABLO GALLEGO

Badger Publishing Limited
Oldmedow Road,
Hardwick Industrial Estate,
King's Lynn PE30 4JJ

Telephone**: 01438 791037**
www.badgerlearning.co.uk

2 4 6 8 10 9 7 5 3

Nightmare of the Scarecrows
ISBN 978-1-78147-493-8

Text © Ian MacDonald 2014
Complete work © Badger Publishing Limited 2014

The right of Ian MacDonald to be identified as author of
this Work has been asserted by him in accordance with the Copyright,
Designs and Patents Act 1988.

Publisher: Susan Ross
Senior Editor: Danny Pearson
Illustration: Mark Penman
Designer: Cathryn Gilbert

Contents

Cast of Characters

Safi

Josh

Milo

Vocabulary

batteries

churchyard

competition

lazily

magnets

metalwork

nightmare

scarecrows

stumble

terrifying

Chapter One

Miss Simms hands out the magnets, but everyone is more interested in talking about the scarecrow competition.

What's yours going to be?

Mine's a bride. I've got my mum's old wedding dress.

Josh and Safi are keeping quiet. They want to win the prize.

Hey, Josh, let's meet after school ...

Will do!

and bring an old bike from your dad's scrapyard.

Chapter Two

The next day at school there's been a break in.

Hey, someone's stolen my computer game!

... and *all* the wires and batteries have gone from the science room!

HUH! Look at the scarecrows.

After lunch the children set up their scarecrows in the town square for the competition.

But later, back at school in the computer room ...

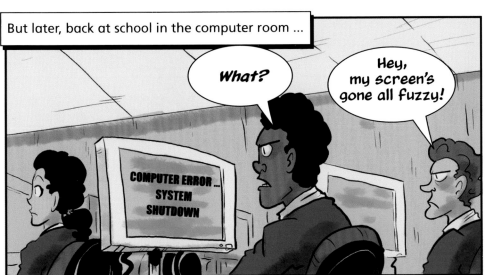

All the lights go out ...

... then slowly, the door opens.

A figure stands in the doorway ...

Chapter Three

Safi and Josh set off on their bikes to search for the scarecrows.

As Josh and Safi wheel their bikes across the square, the sky grows dark and it begins to rain.

Just then a deafening crash of thunder booms overhead …

The bride and groom jerk into life ...
and begin to stumble towards Safi and Josh.

Chapter Four

As Josh and Safi head back to the High Street, they are met by a terrifying sight ...

The first scarecrow turns and looks …

… then another …

… then another.

Then they begin to come towards the girl on the bike.

Chapter Five

At Oakleaf School everything returns to normal once again.

A butterfly dances through the open window.

White clouds drift lazily across a blue sky.

One jolly scarecrow is standing in the cornfield.

Story Facts

Scarecrows were used by the Ancient Egyptians more than 3000 years ago.

In Victorian times small children, called bird-scarers, were paid to scare birds away from the farmers' crops using wooden clappers.

Scarecrows have appeared in many films and stories, like the scarecrow in **The Wizard of Oz** who only wanted a brain.

Nowadays, towns and villages across the country hold competitions to see who can make the best scarecrow.

Questions

1. What are Elm Class learning about in science?

2. What went missing from the science room?

3. Which scarecrow appeared in the doorway of the computer room?

4. Why did Safi want the scarecrows to follow her?

5. Why do you think scarecrows have appeared in so many films and stories?

Meet the Author

Ian MacDonald began writing while working as a teacher in Kent. His stories are full of weird and wonderful characters ... strange aliens, marauding mummies and ghastly gangsters. He shares his writing desk with a cat called Stanley.

Meet the Illustrator

Mark Penman is a lumbering moustachioed grump who when not grouching at people likes to draw comics and watch copious amounts of cartoons. He suspects he may actually be a Viking but is waiting for his beard to be long enough to plait so he can test the theory.